The Usborne
Big Phonics
Workbook

Written by Mairi Mackinnon,

Illustrated by Fred Blunt

Reading and handwriting consultants:
Alison Kelly and Anne Washtell, University of Roehampton

Part 1

satpinmd

Find the big **S** on the sticker pages and stick it here.

Say the sound: sssss
Write a big **S** in the air.
Write **S** with your finger on the table.

Colour in all the things below that begin with **S**.
Put blue **S** stickers next to those pictures.

Did you colour in sun, sock and scissors?
Give yourself a star from the sticker pages.

WELL DONE!

Hungry frogs

Give each frog a long curly tongue so it can catch a bug for its supper.
Start at the bug and follow the curves into the frog's mouth.
You can draw more bubbles and frogspawn in the pond, too.

Trace the **S** with your pencil and write some more. Start at the dot:

Sam the chef needs to hang up his saucepans.
Draw some **S**-shaped hooks for him. Then choose some pans from the sticker pages
and hang them on the hooks.

What is Sam making for supper? Is it sausages, soup, sardines or sauce?
Can you draw it in his pan?

Find the big **a** on the sticker pages and stick it here.

Say the sound: a-a-a-
Write a big **a** in the air.
Write **a** with your finger on the table.

Colour in all the things below that begin with **a**.
Put red **a** stickers next to those pictures.

Did you colour in apple, ambulance and anchor?
Give yourself a star from the sticker pages.

WELL DONE!

Apples and ants

Finish drawing around the apple shapes below.
Start from the dots just under the stalks. Then you can choose
some ants from the sticker pages and add them to the picture.

Trace the **a** with your pencil and write some more:

a a a a

It's time for the school photograph at Additup Academy.
The boys are standing at the back, the girls are sitting down in front.
Finish the girls' faces with **a** shapes.

Adam, Alice, Akram, Amina...
Can you think of any more names beginning with **a**?

Find the big **t** on the sticker pages and stick it here.

Say the sound: t-t-t-
Write a big **t** in the air.
Write **t** with your finger on the table.

Colour in all the things below that begin with **t**.
Put yellow **t** stickers next to those pictures.

Did you colour in tiger, teapot and tent?
Give yourself a star from the sticker pages.

WELL
DONE!

Teddies in the rain

Terrible weather today! Draw some umbrella handles so these teddies can hold up their umbrellas and not get wet. You can colour in the umbrellas, too.

Trace the **t** with your pencil and write some more:

These ships need anchors! Finish the anchors with **t** shapes, then choose turtles from the sticker pages to stick in the water around them.

p

Find the big **p** on the sticker pages and stick it here.

Say the sound: p-p-p-
Write a big **p** in the air.
Write **p** with your finger on the table.

Colour in all the things below that begin with **p**.
Put pink **p** stickers next to those pictures.

Did you colour in pirate, pencil, pear and pumpkin?
Give yourself a star from the sticker pages.

WELL DONE!

Penguins in the park

These penguins are having fun! Can you find:

- a penguin family having a picnic
- baby penguins paddling in the pool
- two penguins playing ping-pong
- a penguin playing the piano
- a penguin painting a picture
- a penguin in a parachute?

When you have found them,
put orange (P) stickers next to them.

Can you spot any more
things beginning with **p**?

Trace the **p** with your pencil and write some more:

p p p

Poppy and Patrick are in the parrot house at the zoo. Finish drawing around the parrots' bodies and tails using **p** shapes. Then choose some flying parrots and parakeets from the sticker pages, and add them to the picture.

Making words

Put **s - a - t** together and you get **sat**.
Read the letters, then read the word, then write it.

s a t   sat   sat

What do you get if you put **p - a - t** together?
Read the letters, then read the word, then write it.

p a t   pat   pat

How about **t - a - p**?

t a p   tap   tap

Which of these pictures is right for sat? Write **sat** underneath:

1   2   3

....

Which of these pictures is right for pat? Write **pat** underneath:

4   5   6

....

Which of these pictures is right for tap? Write **tap** underneath:

7   8   9

....

Did you write **sat** for picture 3, **pat** for picture 5 and **tap** for picture 7?
Give yourself a star from the sticker pages.

WELL
DONE!

Find the big **i** on the sticker pages and stick it here.

Say the sound: i-i-i-
Write a big **i** in the air.
Write **i** with your finger on the table.

Colour in all the things below that begin with **i**.
Put orange **i** stickers next to those pictures.

Did you colour in igloo and ink?
Give yourself a star from the sticker pages.

WELL DONE!

Incomplete insects

All insects should have six legs - but some of the ones below don't!
Can you finish them off so that each insect has enough?

Trace the **i** with your pencil and write some more.
Start with the lines, then add the dots.

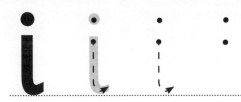

Isabelle and Imran both have their birthday today. Can you finish drawing the candles on their birthday cakes using **i** shapes? Then choose some presents from the sticker pages and stick them on the table.

Find the big **n** on the sticker pages and stick it here.

Say the sound: nnnnn
Write a big **n** in the air.
Write **n** with your finger on the table.

Colour in all the things below that begin with **n**.
Put green **n** stickers next to those pictures.

Did you colour in nest, nail, nurse and net?
Give yourself a star from the sticker pages.

WELL DONE!

N-N-N-Nessie!

This fisherman needn't be nervous - the three beasties are quite friendly. Draw around their humps, starting at the dots.

Trace the **n** with your pencil and write some more:

n n n n

These nine fine elephants are out on parade.
Finish their heads with **n** shapes, then choose some
baby elephant stickers from the sticker pages.

Making words

Put **s - i - p** together and you get **sip**.
Read the letters, then read the word, then write it.

s i p   sip   sip

What do you get if you put **t - i - p** together?
Read the letters, then read the word, then write it.

t i p   tip   tip

How about **p - i - n**?

p i n   pin   pin

Which of these pictures is right for sip? Write **sip** underneath:

1

2

3

Which of these pictures is right for tip? Write **tip** underneath:

4   5   6

....

Which of these pictures is right for pin? Write **pin** underneath:

7   8   9

....

Did you write **sip** for picture 2, **tip** for picture 4 and **pin** for picture 9?
Give yourself a star from the sticker pages.

WELL
DONE!

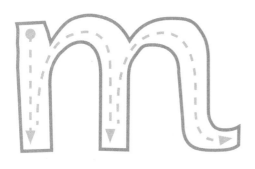

Find the big **m** on the sticker pages and stick it here.

Say the sound: mmmm
Write a big **m** in the air.
Write **m** with your finger on the table.

Colour in all the things below that begin with **m**.
Put purple **m** stickers next to those pictures.

Did you colour in moon, monkey, mushroom and mouse?
Give yourself a star from the sticker pages.

WELL DONE!

Munch munch

These mice need to reach the cheese quickly!
Draw around their ears so that they can hear
if Max the marmalade cat wakes up,
and scurry away to safety.

Trace the **m** with your pencil and write some more:

m m m m

Molly, Minna and Marlon have gone diving. Can you finish their masks using **m** shapes? Then add some tropical fish from the sticker pages. And - the divers haven't noticed, but could that be a mermaid below them?

Find the big **d** on the sticker pages and stick it here.

Say the sound: d-d-d-
Write a big **d** in the air.
Write **d** with your finger on the table.

Colour in all the things below that begin with **d**.
Put blue **d** stickers next to those pictures.

Did you colour in doll, duck, donkey and dog?
Give yourself a star from the sticker pages.

WELL DONE!

Dinosaurs galore

These dinos are doing all kinds of different things.
Can you spot:

- two dinosaurs dancing
- a dinosaur diving into the deep blue sea
- three dinosaurs having a delicious dinner
- a dinosaur dentist
- a dinosaur detective making a discovery?

When you have found them,
put red **d** stickers next to them.

Can you spot any more things
beginning with **d**?

Trace the **d** with your pencil and write some more:

Daisy, David and Daniel are feeding bread to the ducks. Can you finish the ducks' bodies using **d** shapes? Then choose some little ducklings from the sticker pages.

Making words

Put **m - a - t** together and you get **mat**.
Read the letters, then read the word, then write it.

m a t   mat   *mat*

What do you get if you put **m - a - n** together?
Read the letters, then read the word, then write it.

m a n   man   *man*

How about **s - a - d**?

s a d   sad   *sad*

Which of these pictures is right for mat? Write **mat** underneath:

1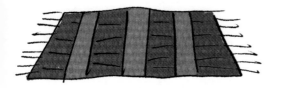

2

3

Which of these pictures is right for man? Write **man** underneath:

4

5

6

....

Which of these pictures is right for sad? Write **sad** underneath:

7

8

9

....

Did you write **mat** for picture 1, **man** for picture 6 and **sad** for picture 8?
Give yourself a star from the sticker pages.

WELL
DONE!

Capital letters

You use capital letters at the beginning of a name or a sentence.
Trace and then copy the pairs of capital letters and small letters below.
Start with the dotted line.

Ss   Aa   Tt

Pp   Ii   Nn

Mm   Dd

WELL DONE!

Part 2

gockckeur

g

Find the big **g** on the sticker pages and stick it here.

Say the sound: g-g-g-
Write a big **g** in the air.
Write **g** with your finger on the table.

Colour in all the things below that begin with **g**.
Put purple **g** stickers next to those pictures.

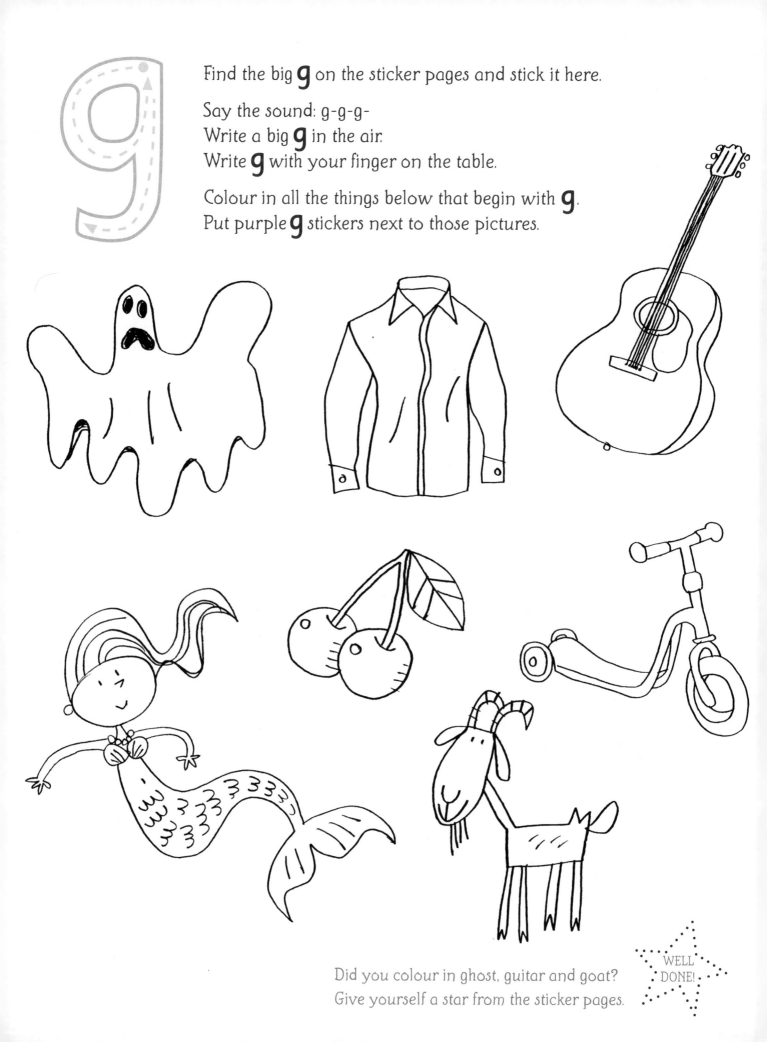

Did you colour in ghost, guitar and goat?
Give yourself a star from the sticker pages.

WELL DONE!

Musical cats

Goodness, gracious, what's going on? The guitar is playing and the cats are singing along. Draw around their bodies and their curly tails, starting at the dot. Then give them some more guitars from the sticker pages.

Trace the **g** with your pencil and write some more. Start at the dot:

g g

Gone fishing... These gorillas need some fish hooks on their lines. Draw some **g**-shaped hooks, then add some fish from the sticker pages. The gorilla on the left looks rather surprised, what do you think he has caught?

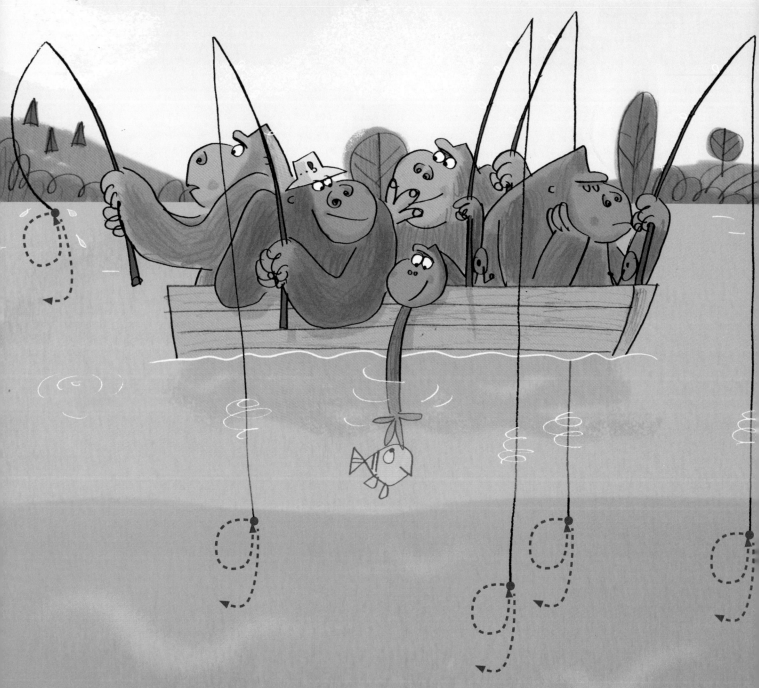

Find the big **O** on the sticker pages and stick it here.

Say the sound: o-o-o-
Write a big **O** in the air.
Write **O** with your finger on the table.

Colour in all the things below that begin with **O**.
Put orange **O** stickers next to those pictures.

Did you colour in orange, octopus, ostrich and otter?
Give yourself a star from the sticker pages.

WELL
DONE!

Off we go!

Draw around the wheels in the picture below. Make sure you draw in the direction of the arrows, though, or everyone will be going backwards!

Trace the **O** with your pencil and write some more:

The Oddbody family have gone to the optician's. Draw around the frames of their smart new glasses using **O** shapes. Then choose more fun frames from the sticker pages, and stick them on the racks behind.

Making words

Put **d - i - g** together and you get **dig**.
Read the letters, then read the word, then write it.

d i g   dig   dig

What do you get if you put **m - o - p** together?
Read the letters, then read the word, then write it.

m o p   mop   mop

How about **d - o - g**?

d o g   dog   dog

Which of these pictures is right for dig? Write **dig** underneath:

1

2

3

Which of these pictures is right for mop? Write **mop** underneath:

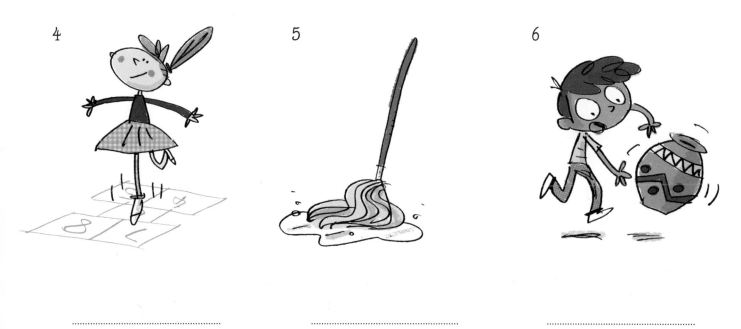

4   5   6

....

Which of these pictures is right for dog? Write **dog** underneath:

7   8   9

....

Did you write **dig** for picture 3, **mop** for picture 5 and **dog** for picture 7?
Give yourself a star from the sticker pages.

WELL DONE!

Find the big **C** on the sticker pages and stick it here.

Say the sound: c-c-c-
Write a big **C** in the air.
Write **C** with your finger on the table.

Colour in all the things below that begin with **C**.
Put pink **C** stickers next to those pictures.

Did you colour in castle, cat, cow, car and camel?
Give yourself a star from the sticker pages.

WELL DONE!

Count the cows

It's a busy day in Cowtown. Can you find:

- a cow cutting a cake
- a cow carrying a cup of coffee
- a cow camping
- a cow conducting a concert
- a cow cooking
- a cow colouring on card

When you have found them,
put red **C** stickers next to them.

Can you spot any more
things beginning with **C**?

Trace the **C** with your pencil and write some more:

C C C

Cassy Croc has made tea for the whole family. Finish the cups and teapot with **C** shapes, then choose some delicious cupcakes from the sticker pages for the cake stand.

k

Find the big **k** on the sticker pages and stick it here.

Say the sound: k-k-k-
Write a big **k** in the air.
Write **k** with your finger on the table.

Colour in all the things below that begin with **k**.
Put blue **k** stickers next to those pictures.

Did you colour in kangaroo, kite, key and king?
Give yourself a star from the sticker pages.

WELL DONE!

Cluck cluck!

These four hungry hens need beaks to eat up their corn.
Finish their beaks with **k** shapes, then add some chickens
from the sticker pages.

Trace the **k** with your pencil and write some more:

k k k k

It's so breezy today, Kelvin, Kieran and Katie Mouse have been swept up in the air with their kites. Finish the kite tails with **k** shapes, then colour in the kites. Don't worry, the mice will soon be floating down safely.

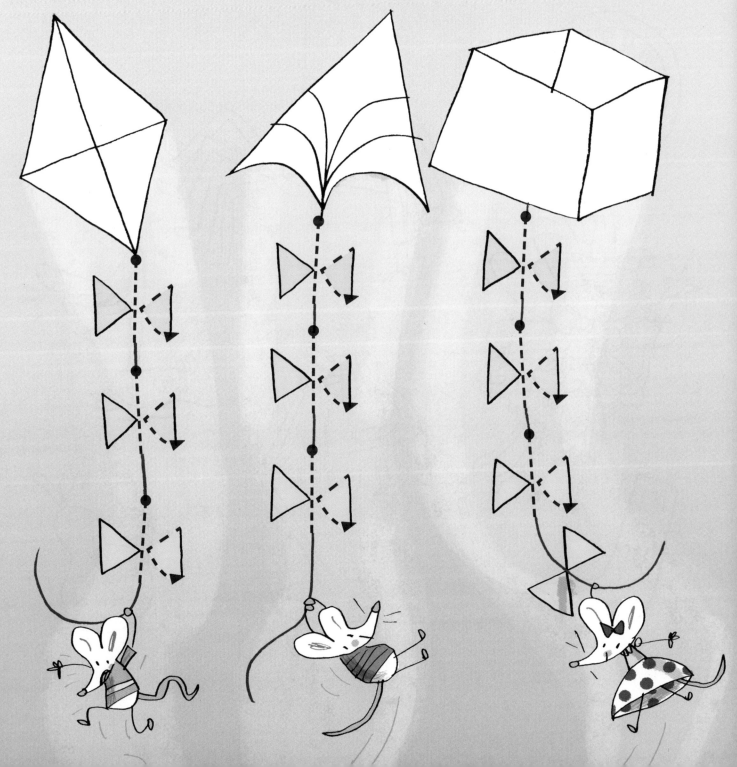

Put **c** and **k** together and you get **ck**. **ck** makes the same sound as either **c** or **k**. Find the big **ck** on the sticker pages and stick it here.

Say the sound: ck-ck-ck-

ck is most often found in the middle or at the end of a word. Colour in all the things below that end with **ck**. Put red **ck** stickers next to those pictures.

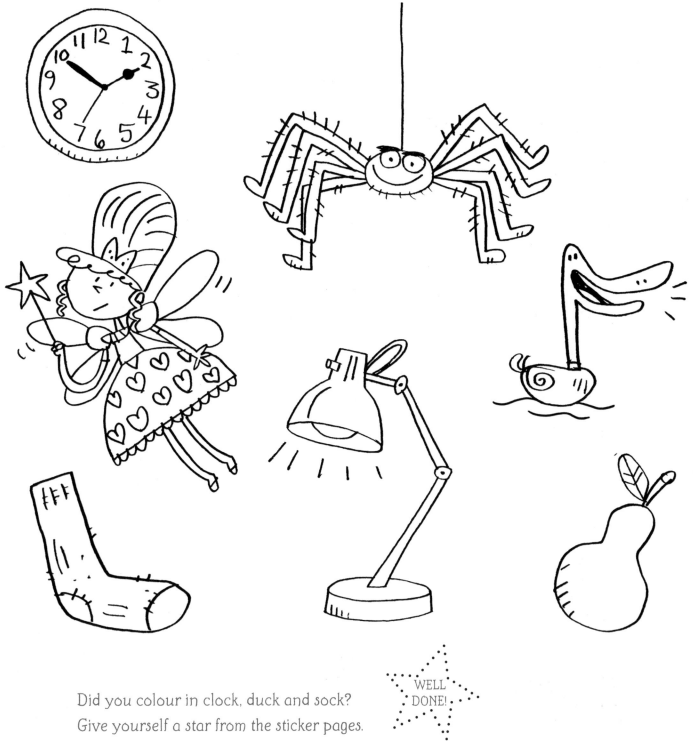

Did you colour in clock, duck and sock? Give yourself a star from the sticker pages.

WELL DONE!

Trace the **ck** with your pencil and write some more:

ck ck ck

Granny Beck is filling in her photo album. Help her by finishing all the names with **ck**.

Rick

Nick

Jack

Jock

Making words

Put **c - a - p** together and you get **cap**.
Read the letters, then read the word, then write it.

c a p   cap   cap

What do you get if you put **s - o - ck** together?
Read the letters, then read the word, then write it.

s o ck   sock   sock

How about **k - i - ck**?

k i ck   kick   kick

Which of these pictures is right for cap? Write **cap** underneath:

1

2

3

Which of these pictures is right for sock? Write **sock** underneath:

4

5

6

....

Which of these pictures is right for kick? Write **kick** underneath:

7

8

9

....

Did you write **cap** for picture 1, **sock** for picture 6 and **kick** for picture 8?
Give yourself a star from the sticker pages.

WELL DONE!

Find the big **e** on the sticker pages and stick it here.

Say the sound: e-e-e-
Write a big **e** in the air.
Write **e** with your finger on the table.

Colour in all the things below that begin with **e**.
Put light blue **e** stickers next to those pictures.

Did you colour in elephant, egg and elf?
Give yourself a star from the sticker pages.

WELL DONE!

Elevated elephants

These elephants are on the wing, and it's ever so exciting. Every elephant should try it! Draw around the loops, then think what else (or who else) might be up in the air and draw it in the spaces.

Trace the **e** with your pencil and write some more:

Finish the fish below with **e** shapes. Then choose some eels (electric eels, of course) from the sticker pages to stick in among them.

Find the big **u** on the sticker pages and stick it here.

Say the sound: u-u-u-
Write a big **u** in the air.
Write **u** with your finger on the table.

Not many things begin with **u**. Can you find one below?
Colour it in and put a green **u** sticker next to the picture.

Did you colour in the umbrella?
Give yourself a star from the sticker pages.

WELL
DONE!

Under the umbrellas

It's a lovely afternoon in Upton-on-Sea. Mr. and Mrs. Underwood are drinking tea in the shade, and Umberto is selling plenty of ice cream. Finish the trimming on their umbrellas, starting from the dots.

Trace the **u** with your pencil and write some more:

u u u i

Draw **u** shapes to make a feather pattern on this little owl's body.
Then choose stars from the sticker pages to stick in the sky all around.

Making words

Put **n - e - t** together and you get **net**.
Read the letters, then read the word, then write it.

n e t   net   net

What do you get if you put **c - u - t** together?
Read the letters, then read the word, then write it.

c u t   cut   cut

How about **d - u - ck**?

d u ck   duck   duck

Which of these pictures is right for net? Write **net** underneath:

1

2

3

Which of these pictures is right for cut? Write **cut** underneath:

4   5   6

....

Which of these pictures is right for duck? Write **duck** underneath:

7   8   9

....

Did you write **net** for picture 3, **cut** for picture 4 and **duck** for picture 8?
Give yourself a star from the sticker pages.

WELL DONE!

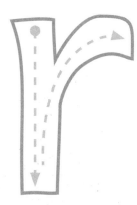

Find the big **r** on the sticker pages and stick it here.

Say the sound: rrrrrr
Write a big **r** in the air.
Write **r** with your finger on the table.

Colour in all the things below that begin with **r**.
Put yellow **r** stickers next to those pictures.

Did you colour in rabbit, rhino, ring, robot and rose?
Give yourself a star from the sticker pages.

WELL
DONE!

Run, rabbits!

Some of these rabbits are having a race, rushing about all over the place, while others are resting. Finish their ears with **r** shapes, starting from the dots, then add some baby rabbits from the sticker pages.

Trace the **r** with your pencil and write some more:

Finish the reindeer's antlers with **r** shapes. Then complete the scene with robins and snowflakes from the sticker pages. Do you recognize the reindeer in the middle?

Making words

Put **r - a - t** together and you get **rat**.
Read the letters, then read the word, then write it.

r a t rat rat

What do you get if you put **r - u - g** together?
Read the letters, then read the word, then write it.

rug rug rug

Which of these pictures is right for rat? Write **rat** underneath:

1

2

3

Which of these pictures is right for rug? Write **rug** underneath:

4

5

6

Did you write **rat** for picture 1 and **rug** for picture 5?
Give yourself a star from the sticker pages.

WELL DONE!

Capital letters

You use capital letters at the beginning of a name or a sentence.
Trace and then copy the pairs of capital letters and small letters below.
Start with the dotted line.

Gg

Oo

Cc

Kk

Ee

Uu

Rr

Part 3

h b l ll f ff ss

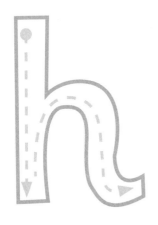

Find the big **h** on the sticker pages and stick it here.

Say the sound: h-h-h-
Write a big **h** in the air.
Write **h** with your finger on the table.

Colour in all the things below that begin with **h**.
Put blue **h** stickers next to those pictures.

Did you colour in helicopter, horse, hippo, house and helmet?
Give yourself a star from the sticker pages.

WELL DONE!

Hippo heaven

Heavens above, how many hippos is that?
Can you find:

- a hippo playing a harp
- some hippos singing hymns
- a hippo playing hopscotch
- two hippos hugging
- some hippos playing hockey
- a hippo hang-gliding?

When you have found them,
put a **h** sticker next to them.

Can you spot any more
things beginning with **h**?

Hold your horses

Have you heard? There's a grand tournament today. Sir Harold, Sir Hugo, Sir Hector, Sir Humphrey and Sir Hubert are all waiting to saddle up. Finish drawing their horses, starting at the dots, then choose helmets for the five knights from the sticker pages.

Trace the **h** with your pencil and write some more. Start at the dot:

h h h

These hungry monkeys are happy – they've found a whole heap of delicious ripe bananas. Finish drawing around the bananas with **h** shapes, then add some baby monkeys from the sticker pages.

Find the big **b** on the sticker pages and stick it here.

Say the sound: b-b-b-

Write a big **b** in the air.

Write **b** with your finger on the table.

Colour in all the things below that begin with **b**.

Put yellow **b** stickers next to those pictures.

Did you colour in balloon, bicycle, baby, boot and butterfly?

Give yourself a star from the sticker pages.

WELL DONE!

Busy bears

It's a bear bonanza! Can you find:

- a bear doing ballet
- a bear playing the bagpipes
- a bear blowing bubbles
- some bears playing baseball
- a bear on a bicycle?

When you have found them,
put a (b) sticker next to them.

Can you spot any more
things beginning with b?

Snail race

Boris the snail is in the lead, he's almost reached the top of his flower stem. Draw around his body and his shell, starting at the dot, then draw around his friends' shells too. (Can you think of some more names beginning with **b** for them?) Then add some buzzy bees from the sticker pages.

Trace the **b** with your pencil and write some more. Start at the dot:

Bill Barker and his boys are busy down on the farm. It's very wet and muddy and they had all better wear boots. Can you finish drawing their boots with **b** shapes?

Making words

Put **h - e - n** together and you get **hen**.
Read the letters, then read the word, then write it.

h e n   hen   hen

What do you get if you put **b - a - ck** together?
Read the letters, then read the word, then write it.

b a ck   back   back

How about **h - a - t**?

h a t   hat   hat

Which of these pictures is right for hen? Write **hen** underneath:

1

2

3

Which of these pictures is right for back? Write **back** underneath:

4

5

6

....

Which of these pictures is right for hat? Write **hat** underneath:

7

8

9

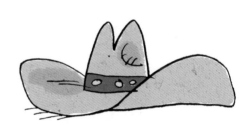

....

Did you write **hen** for picture 2, **back** for picture 4 and **hat** for picture 9?
Give yourself a star from the sticker pages.

WELL
DONE!

Find the big **l** on the sticker pages and stick it here.

Say the sound: lllll
Write a big **l** in the air.
Write **l** with your finger on the table.

Colour in all the things below that begin with **l**.
Put orange **l** stickers next to those pictures.

Did you colour in ladder, leaf, letter and lighthouse?
Give yourself a star from the sticker pages.

WELL DONE!

Lions in the library

Look at all these lions! Can you spot:

- a lion up a ladder
- a lion reading a letter
- a lion in a lifejacket
- a lion drinking lemonade
- a lion with a lamp
- a leopard looking lost?

When you have found them, put a Ⓛ sticker next to them.

Can you spot any more things beginning with l?

Lizard lunch

Have you ever seen lizards flicking out their long tongues? They are lightning fast, so you have to look hard. These lucky lizards are snapping up some unlucky bugs for their lunch. Finish drawing their tongues, then add some bugs from the sticker pages.

Trace the **l** with your pencil and write some more. Start at the dot:

The lemurs are having a lovely lazy afternoon. Finish their tails with **l** shapes, then choose some feathery leaves from the sticker pages to stick on the branches.

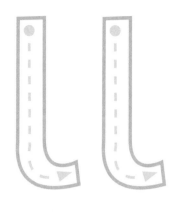

ll makes the same sound as l. Find the big ll on the sticker pages and stick it here.

Say the sound: llll

ll is most often found in the middle or at the end of a word.
Colour in all the things below that end with ll.
Put blue ll stickers next to those pictures.

Did you colour in bull, bell, shell, hill and doll?
Give yourself a star from the sticker pages.

WELL DONE!

A Tree full of Bells

Ella Bell has been finding out all about her family tree. These Bells lived over a hundred years ago. Help Ella to finish writing all their names.

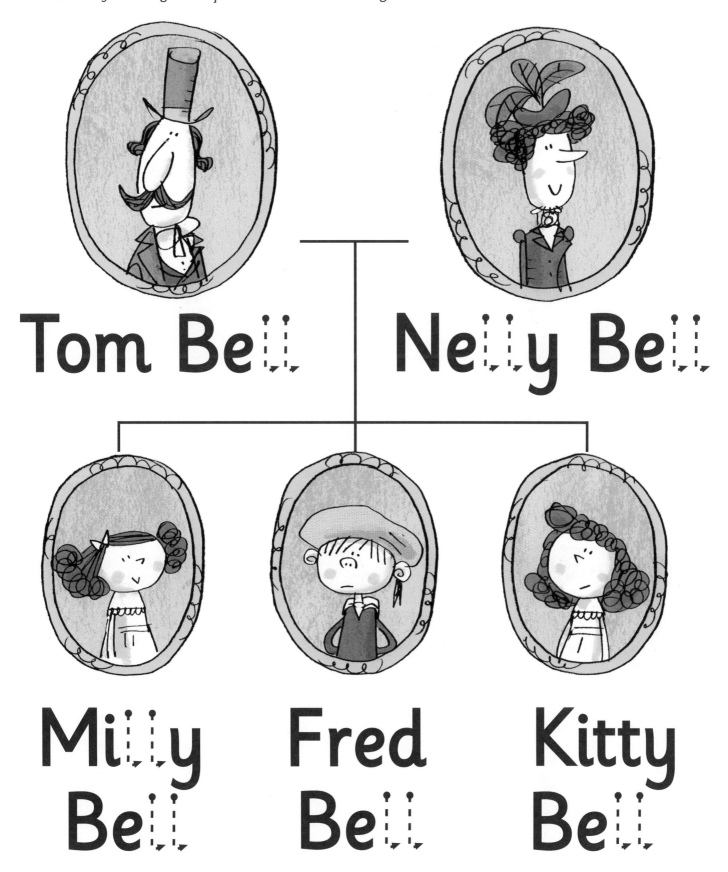

Tom Bell   Nelly Bell

Milly Bell   Fred Bell   Kitty Bell

Making words

Put **l - o - ck** together and you get **lock.**
Read the letters, then read the word, then write it.

l o ck   lock   lock

What do you get if you put **l - e - g** together?
Read the letters, then read the word, then write it.

l e g   leg   leg

How about **b - e - ll** ?

b e ll   bell   bell

Which of these pictures is right for lock? Write **lock** underneath:

1

2

3

Which of these pictures is right for leg? Write **leg** underneath:

4

5

6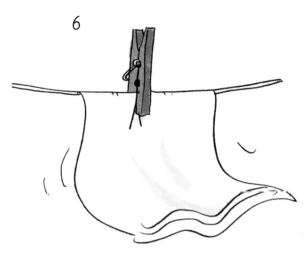

....

Which of these pictures is right for bell? Write **bell** underneath:

7

8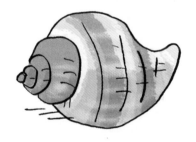

9

....

Did you write **lock** for picture 3, **leg** for picture 5 and **bell** for picture 7? Give yourself a star from the sticker pages.

WELL DONE!

f

Find the big **f** on the sticker pages and stick it here.

Say the sound: ffff
Write a big **f** in the air.
Write **f** with your finger on the table.

Colour in all the things below that begin with **f**.
Put green **f** stickers next to those pictures.

Did you colour in fairy, fan, fish and feather?
Give yourself a star from the sticker pages.

WELL DONE!

Fantastic fish

These fish are having fun! Can you find:

- some fish playing football
- a fish making a funny face
- five fish following each other
- a fish having a fizzy drink
- a fish dressed up as a fairy
- a fish with a fan?

When you have found them, put a **f** sticker next to them.

Can you spot any more things beginning with **f**?

Feathery fins

Far below the sea surface, these seahorses are having a fine time. Finish drawing their bodies, starting at the dot, then choose some fancy fish from the sticker pages to stick in the water around them.

Trace the **f** with your pencil and write some more. Start at the dot:

These four fairies have been finding flowers to decorate the Fabulous Fairy Fête. Draw in the flower stems using **f** shapes.

ff makes the same sound as **f**. Find the big **ff** on the sticker pages and stick it here.

Say the sound: ffff

ff is most often found in the middle or at the end of a word. Colour in all the things below that end with **ff**. Put red **ff** stickers next to those pictures.

Did you colour in cliff and sheriff?
Give yourself a star from the sticker pages.

WELL DONE!

Off they go!

The foxes are having a piggyback race, and they're finding it's hard work. Look at them all, puffing and panting! Finish off their speech bubbles, then add some woodland creatures from the sticker pages to watch the race.

Making words

Put **f** - **a** - **n** together and you get **fan.**
Read the letters, then read the word, then write it.

f a n   fan   fan
....

What do you get if you put **f** - **i** - **n** together?
Read the letters, then read the word, then write it.

f i n   fin   fin
....

How about **r** - **u** - **ff**?

r u ff   ruff   ruff
....

Which of these pictures is right for fan? Write **fan** underneath:

1   2   3

....

Which of these pictures is right for fin? Write **fin** underneath:

4

5

6

....

Which of these pictures is right for ruff? Write **ruff** underneath:

7

8

9

....

Did you write **fan** for picture 1, **fin** for picture 5 and **ruff** for picture 7?
Give yourself a star from the sticker pages.

WELL DONE!

SS makes the same sound as **S**. Find the big **SS** on the sticker pages and stick it here.

Say the sound: ssss

SS is most often found in the middle or at the end of a word. Colour in all the things below that end with **SS**. Put purple **SS** stickers next to those pictures.

Did you colour in compass, glass and dress?
Give yourself a star from the sticker pages.

WELL DONE!

Hissing snakes

Sssscary ssssnakes hissssss a lot – but snakes can be friendly too. Finish the words below, and you'll find a pair that are not hissing but kissing. Then you can add some baby snakes from the sticker pages. Isssn't that sssweet!

hiss

kiss

hiss

hiss

hiss

hiss

Making words

Put **m** - **e** - **ss** together and you get **mess.**
Read the letters, then read the word, then write it.

m e ss mess mess

What do you get if you put **k** - **i** - **ss** together?
Read the letters, then read the word, then write it.

k i ss kiss kiss

How about **b** - **o** - **ss**?

b o ss boss boss

Which of these pictures is right for mess? Write **mess** underneath:

1

2

3

....

Which of these pictures is right for kiss? Write **kiss** underneath:

4

5

6

....

Which of these pictures is right for boss? Write **boss** underneath:

7

8

9

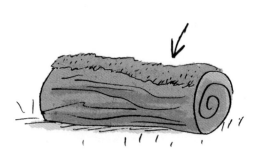

....

Did you write **mess** for picture 3, **kiss** for picture 5 and **boss** for picture 7?
Give yourself a star from the sticker pages.

WELL
DONE!

Capital letters

You use capital letters at the beginning of a name or a sentence.
Trace and then copy the pairs of capital letters and small letters below.
Start with the dotted line.

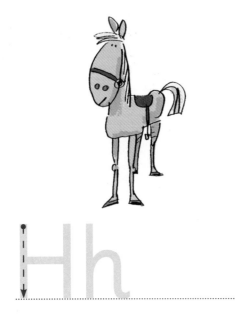

Hh

Bb

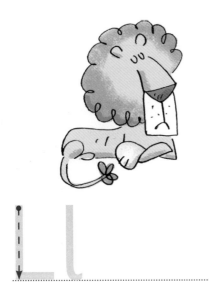

Ll

Ff

Part 4

j q v w x y z zz

Find the big **j** on the sticker pages and stick it here.

Say the sound: j-j-j-j
Write a big **j** in the air.
Write **j** with your finger on the table.

Colour in all the things below that begin with **j**.
Put purple **j** stickers next to those pictures.

Did you colour in jellyfish, juggler and jam?
Give yourself a star from the sticker pages.

WELL DONE!

Jaguar jazz

Down in the jungle, the Joe Jaguar Five are jamming before their big concert later tonight. Finish off their saxophones with **j** shapes, and add **j**s to Jim Jaguar's bass drum. Then add some musical notes from the sticker pages.

Trace the **j** with your pencil and write some more. Start at the smaller dot:

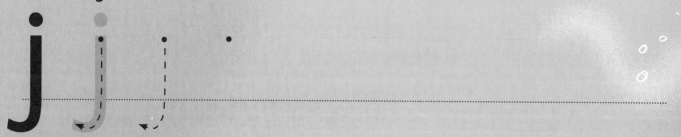

These jolly jellyfish are jiggling and jumping in the warm ocean current. Finish their tentacles with **j** shapes, then choose some more little jellyfish from the sticker pages to swim in the water around them.

Find the big **q** on the sticker pages and stick it here.

Say the sound: qu-qu-qu
Write a big **q** in the air.
Write **q** with your finger on the table.

Not many things begin with **q**. Can you find one below?
Colour it in, and put a green **q** sticker next to the picture.

Did you colour in the queen?
Give yourself a star from the sticker pages.

WELL DONE!

A quantity of queens

These queens are having quite a time! Can you find:

- a queen under a quilt
- a queen sitting quietly
- some queens queuing
- some more queens quarrelling
- a queen quivering and quaking?

When you have found them,
put a **q** sticker next to them.

Trace the **q** with your pencil and write some more:

Quentin the quizmaster is asking some seriously tricky questions. Finish drawing his face and the contestants' faces using **q** shapes, then add some colourful question marks from the sticker pages.

Making words

Put j - e - t together and you get jet.
Read the letters, then read the word, then write it.

j e t jet jet

What do you get if you put j - o - g together?
Read the letters, then read the word, then write it.

j o g jog jog

How about qu - i - ck?

qu i ck quick

Which of these pictures is right for jet? Write jet underneath:

1

2

3

....

Which of these pictures is right for jog? Write **jog** underneath:

4

5

6

....

Which of these pictures is right for quick? Write **quick** underneath:

7

8

9

....

Did you write **jet** for picture 1, **jog** for picture 5 and **quick** for picture 9?
Give yourself a star from the sticker pages.

WELL
DONE!

V

Find the big **V** on the sticker pages and stick it here.

Say the sound: vvvv
Write a big **V** in the air.
Write **V** with your finger on the table.

Colour in all the things below that begin with **V**.
Put red **V** stickers next to those pictures.

Did you colour in violin and volcano?
Give yourself a star from the sticker pages.

WELL
DONE!

Volcano valley

Here's a happy event – this dino mama has four new babies. Draw around the spikes on her back, and also the broken eggshells, using **V** shapes. Then choose pterosaurs from the sticker pages to fly in the sky. Do you notice that their wings can make a **V** shape too?

Trace the **V** with your pencil and write some more:

V V V

Victor, Vernon and Vincent are on their way out for the evening... but don't worry, these vegetarian vampires are only going to watch a game. What will it be, vampire volleyball or werewolf water-polo? Draw in their fangs using **V** shapes, then add some bats from the sticker pages.

Find the big **W** on the sticker pages and stick it here.

Say the sound: w-w-w-w
Write a big **W** in the air.
Write **W** with your finger on the table.

Colour in all the things below that begin with **W**.
Put orange **W** stickers next to those pictures.

Did you colour in watch, windmill and wing?
Give yourself a star from the sticker pages.

WELL
DONE!

Wasps welcome

"What lovely weather, why don't we have a picnic? The humans have left all this food, and we don't want to waste it, do we?" Draw around the wasps' zigzag markings using **W** shapes, then add some butterflies from the sticker pages. Can you spot the **W** patterns on their wings?

Trace the **W** with your pencil and write some more:

W W W W

Wow! Don't Woody and Wendy look wonderful on their wedding day?
Finish all the collars, and also the bows on Wendy's dress, using **W** shapes.

Making words

Put **v** - **a** - **n** together and you get **van**.
Read the letters, then read the word, then write it.

v a n   van   van

What do you get if you put **v** - **e** - **t** together?
Read the letters, then read the word, then write it.

v e t   vet   vet

How about **w** - **e** - **ll**?

w e ll   well   well

Which of these pictures is right for van? Write **van** underneath:

1

2

3

....

Which of these pictures is right for vet? Write **vet** underneath:

4

5

6

....

Which of these pictures is right for well? Write **well** underneath:

7

8

9

....

Did you write **van** for picture 3, **vet** for picture 5 and **well** for picture 7?
Give yourself a star from the sticker pages.

WELL
DONE!

Find the big **X** on the sticker pages and stick it here.

Say the sound: x-x-x-x
Write a big **X** in the air.
Write **X** with your finger on the table.

Colour in all the things below that end with **X**.
Put blue **X** stickers next to those pictures.

Did you colour in box, fox and six?
Give yourself a star from the sticker pages.

WELL DONE!

Foxes with boxes

It's Alex Fox's birthday party, and her friends have brought stacks of presents.
Alex's brother Felix is more interested in eating the birthday cake, though!
Finish the presents by drawing **X**-shaped ribbons on the boxes,
then add some more balloons from the sticker pages.

Trace the **X** with your pencil and write some more:

These three absent-minded pirates have buried their treasure – and then forgotten where they put it! Help them to find the right hiding-places on the map below, and draw **X**s to mark the spots. Can you see any more **X** shapes on the map?

Rory Redbeard needs to climb a fiery mountain...

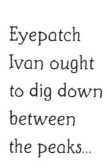

Eyepatch Ivan ought to dig down between the peaks...

...and Pegleg Pete should try raising the roof.

Find the big **y** on the sticker pages and stick it here.

Say the sound: y-y-y-y
Write a big **y** in the air.
Write **y** with your finger on the table.

Colour in all the things below that begin with **y**.
Put green **y** stickers next to those pictures.

Did you colour in yo-yo and yogurt?
Give yourself a star from the sticker pages.

WELL DONE!

The yak pack

Yikes, there are yaks everywhere!
Can you find:

- a yak with a yo-yo
- a yak doing yoga
- a yak yawning
- a yak with a yacht
- a yak eating yogurt?

When you have found them,
put a **y** sticker next to them.

Trace the **y** with your pencil and write some more:

In the high Himalayas, this mountaineer has made a startling discovery. The yeti look pretty surprised, too! Finish drawing their open mouths using **y** shapes, then add some yeti babies from the sticker pages.

Making words

Put **b** - **o** - **x** together and you get **box**.
Read the letters, then read the word, then write it.

b o x   box   box

What do you get if you put **m** - **i** - **x** together?
Read the letters, then read the word, then write it.

m i x   mix   mix

How about **y** - **e** - **ll**?

y e ll   yell   yell

Which of these pictures is right for box? Write **box** underneath:

1

2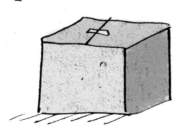

3

....

Which of these pictures is right for mix? Write **mix** underneath:

4

5

6

....

Which of these pictures is right for yell? Write **yell** underneath:

7

8

9

....

Did you write **box** for picture 2, **mix** for picture 4 and **yell** for picture 8?
Give yourself a star from the sticker pages.

WELL DONE!

Find the big **Z** on the sticker pages and stick it here.

Say the sound: zzzz
Write a big **Z** in the air.
Write **Z** with your finger on the table.

Colour in all the things below that begin with **Z**.
Put yellow **Z** stickers next to those pictures.

Did you colour in zebra and zip?
Give yourself a star from the sticker pages.

WELL DONE!

Stormy night

It's a bad night to be out at sea. This brave ship is dodging the storm and steering away from the cliff. Finish drawing the zigzag lightning, then add some more ships from the sticker pages.

Trace the **Z** with your pencil and write some more:

Z Z Z ⋅

Zachary Frog is putting on a talent show tonight. Here are Zander, Zygmund and Zoltan with the all-singing, all-hopping opening number. Finish drawing their legs with **Z** shapes.

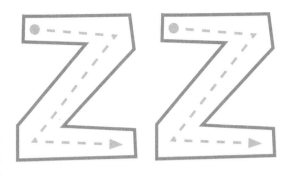

Find the big **ZZ** on the sticker pages and stick it here.

Say the sound: zzzzzz

Colour in all the things below that make a **ZZ** <u>sound</u>. Put pink **ZZ** stickers next to those pictures.

Did you colour in the bee, the wasp and the drill? Give yourself a star from the sticker pages.

WELL DONE!

Snoozing at the zoo

It's a warm summer afternoon, and all the zoo animals are dozing off in the heat. Write **ZZ**s next to all the sleeping creatures, then choose some more buzzy bees and dragonflies from the sticker pages to stick in the spaces around them.

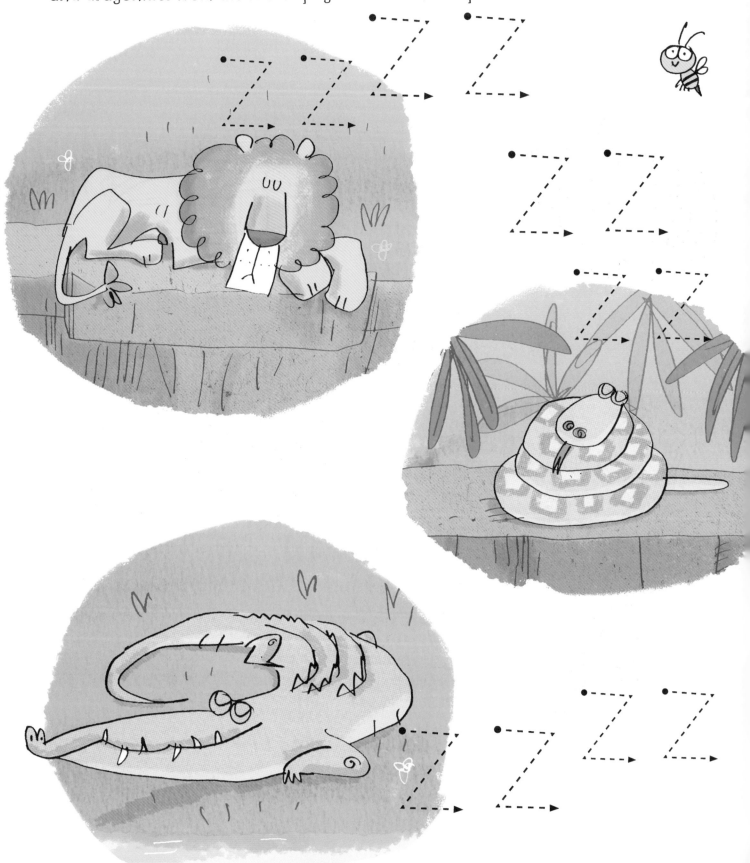

Capital letters

You use capital letters at the beginning of a name or a sentence. Trace and then copy the pairs of capital letters and small letters below. Start with the dotted line.

Designed by Caroline Spatz
Edited by Lesley Sims and Jenny Tyler

i i i i i
i i i

n n n n
n n

m m m m

m m m m

d d d d d

d d d d d

d d

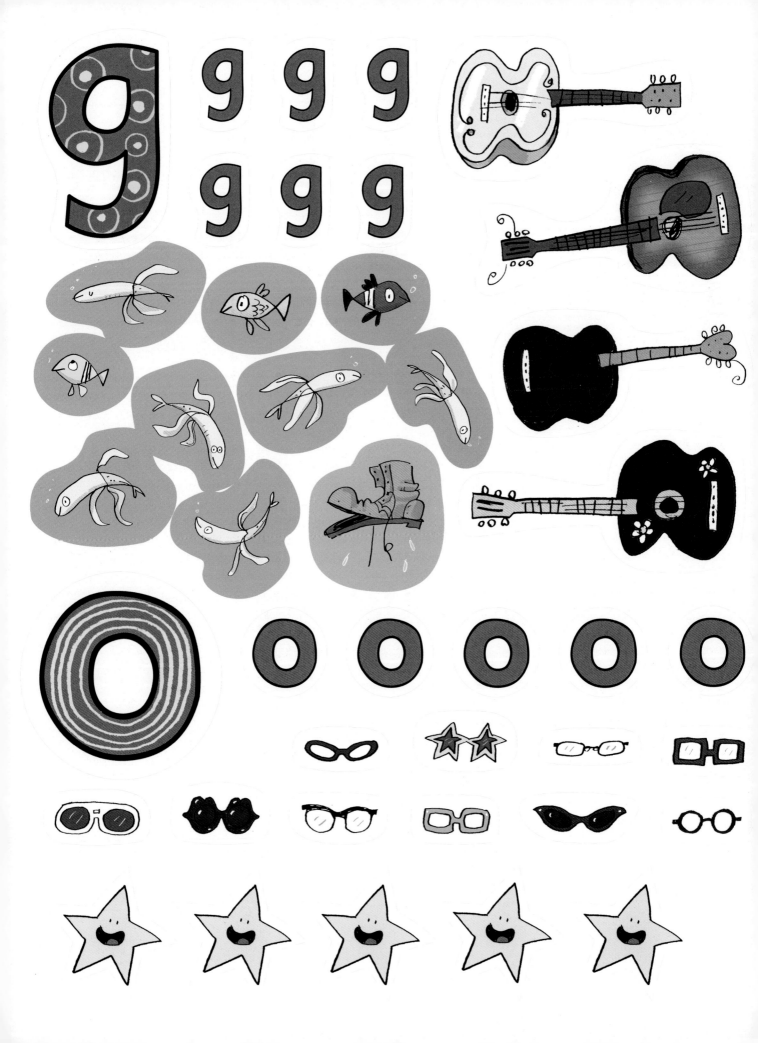

 C C C C C C

 c c c c c c

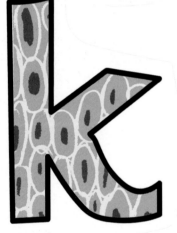 k k k k k

k

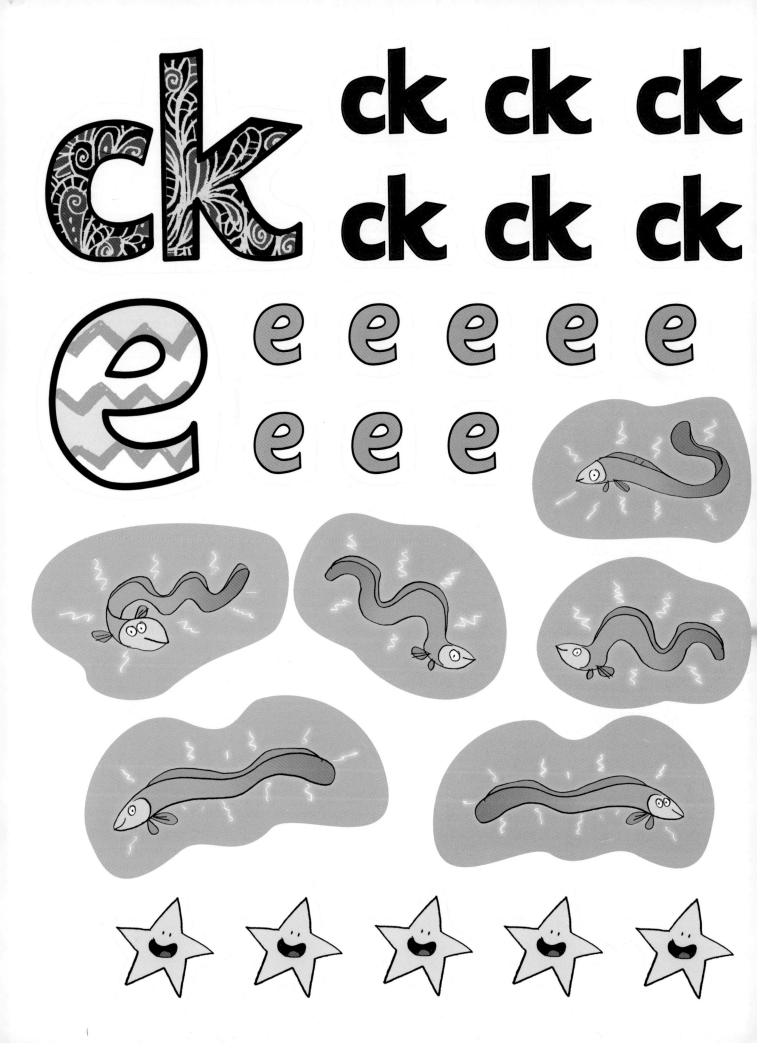

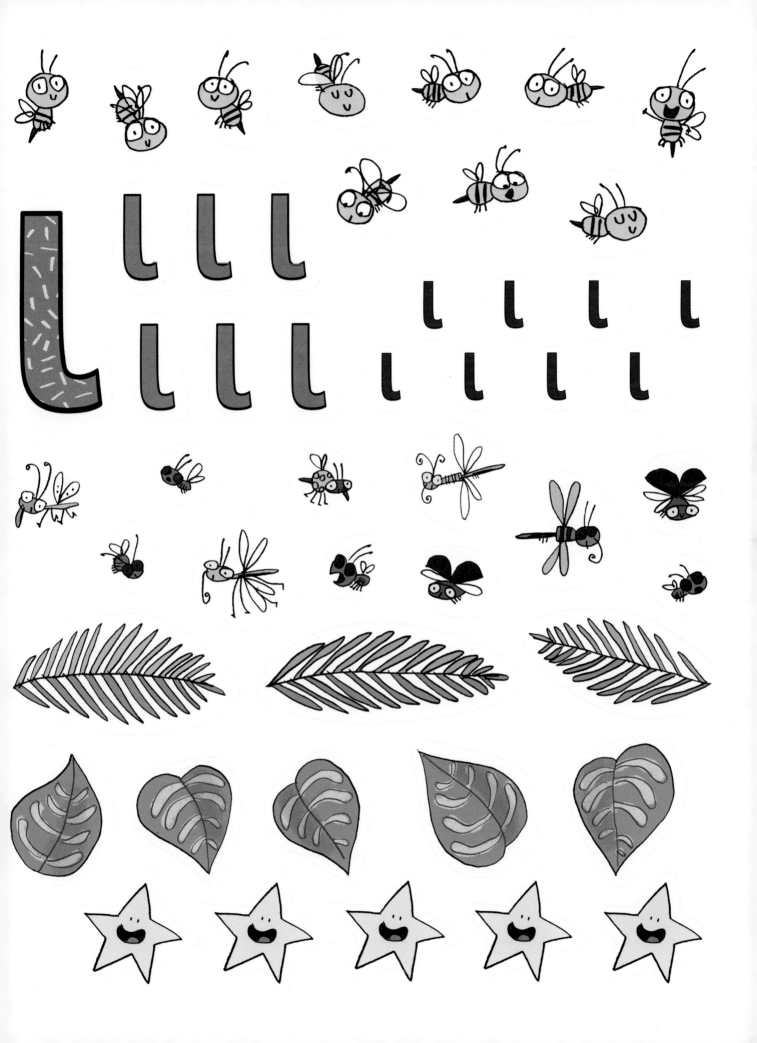

ll   ll

ll   ll   ll   ll   ll

f   f   f   f   f   f   f   f

f   f   f   f   f   f   f

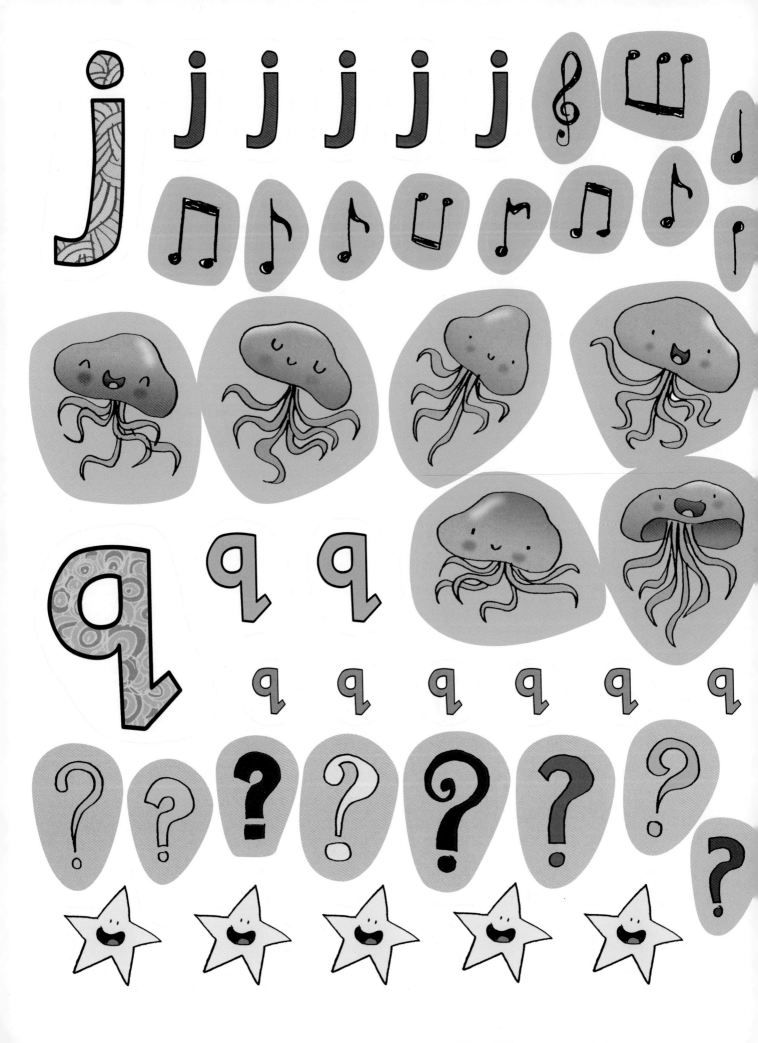